Behind the Scenes:

Social Calendar & Planner
For
The Dogs of Instagram

LOUISE HALL REIDER

This Book
Belongs To:

_____

Contents

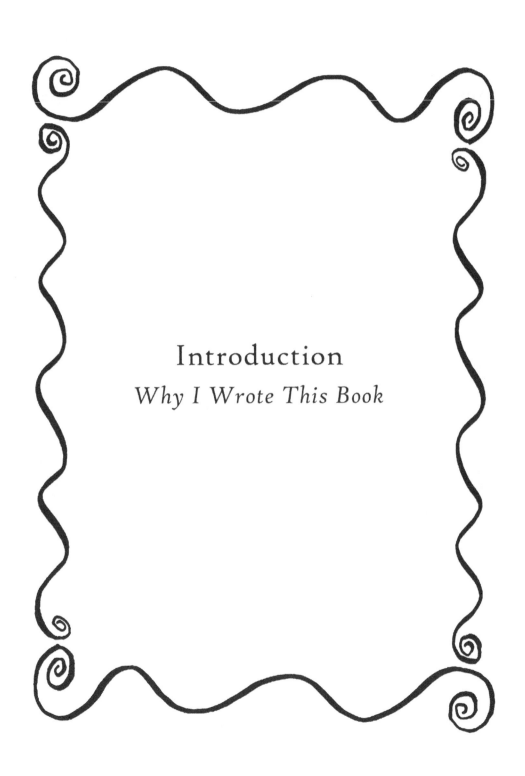

Introduction

Why I Wrote This Book

Introduction

New Concept: A Planner for Insta-Dogs!

Earlier this year, I was astounded by a recurring challenge that came up as I conducted a plethora of interviews for my first book, **"Behind the Scenes: The Mysteries of the Dogs of Instagram."**

So many spoke of no real system to keep track of all the dates and other items needed for their Instagram account. You might be like me – I could relate! I too have struggled to find a way to stay organized for all the accounts and besties to like & comment, their gotcha days, birthdays, gifts, dog mom names, future plans for posts, hashtags to remember, addresses and contact info, along with so many other things.

We need one place to keep track of it all! That is why I put together this new book, **"Behind the Scenes: Social Calendar & Planner for The Dogs of Instagram"**.

Together with quips & quotes there is space for all your personal details, wish lists, party plans, wardrobe inspirations and more. Other sections to fill in include an address book, a month-by month planner, holiday cards and gifts with tracking, new accounts to consider, and websites, magazines, books & blogs to read for inspiration and education.

As an extra bonus we put in a section with intriguing information from InstaFamous influencers who gave us their "Cliff Notes" on how they attracted so many followers and the tips & tricks they learned along the way.

It is my hope this agenda will be an invaluable tool to help streamline our fur babys' accounts and de-stress our days!

It is my hope this agenda will l be an invaluable tool to help streamline our fur babys' accounts and de-stress our days!

Chapter 1
How To Use This Book

Chapter 1

How to Use this Book

Everyone is different ~ so how you use this book will be up to you! There is lots of space to use as you wish.

I suggest for you to decide which sections are most important to you and to start there. There is no need to use all of the sections, only those that will help you stay organized on Instagram.

There are as may ways to use this book as there are Instadogs! For example, the Like, Comment & Save Checklist (Chapter 24) will be my new system of making sure *I* am in charge of who I see on my daily sessions instead of only those IG and the algorithm send me.

Two entire sections, by popular demand, (Chapters 3 & 4) are devoted to keeping track of Besties and their birthdays and other occasions. The first is simply a list of Besties and basic information for each friend at a glance. The next one gives each Bestie two full pages for all their detailed information.

In the corresponding sections, you can list of all your favorite hashtags, hashtags to try, upcoming pawties, events and your best-loved fundraisers.

If you are like me, and love to dream up new ideas, there are many places provided for that. As a start try Chapter 6 for themes and dreams.

The Month-by-Month Planner in Chapter 9 is where it comes together. It is a *perpetual* calendar for year after year, where you can easily see all your important dates to remember in one place.

Another challenge for some is to keep track of their wardrobe items ~ from which designer or shop were they? And what was the name of the proprietor again? (Chapter 11).

One friend has kept all the return addresses of the gifts and cards she has received in a box. In order to organize these for faster retrieval she might tape them all on pages of the address section in Chapter 16. Why not?

If you are more of a digital tracker ~ check out the Book Bonus section for your free gift of a downloadable **digital version** of the address book/holiday card tracking section.

It is my hope you will find the collection of stories at the beginning of each chapter interesting and inspiring, and that you find the random examples I have included delightful. The story of **The Birthday Puppy** in Chapter 6 warmed my heart.

Be creative and in case we did not include something important to you, we made sure to leave plenty of extra space for your personal notes in Chapter 27. So, grab your favorite pen, fill in your desired spaces, find inspiration from others and most importantly ~ Enjoy!

Tip:

For easy access to your favorite chapters, colorful writable tabs are available on Amazon or your office supply store. These can be stuck on and positioned as you wish. They can also be used as alphabet dividers for the address book. We bought the Avery Ultra Tabs for this purpose.

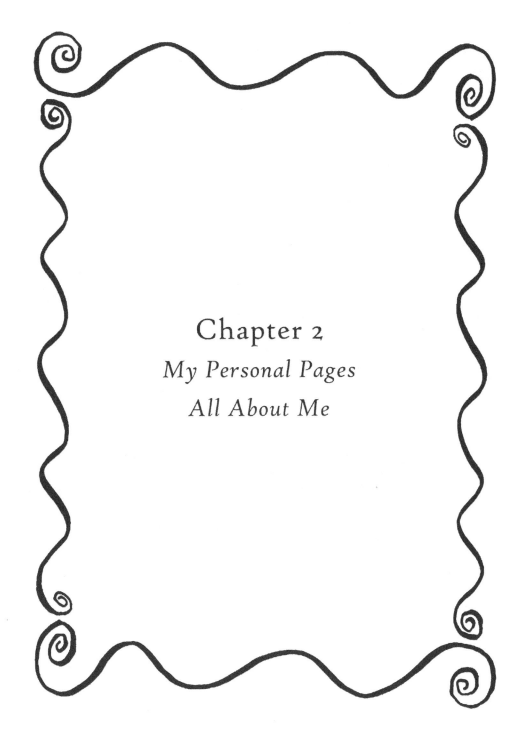

Chapter 2
My Personal Pages
All About Me

My Personal Pages
All About Me

IG Name: _____

Name: _____

Mom/Dad: _____

Other Family: _____

My Birthday: _____

My Gotcha Day: _____

My Measurements: _____

Neck: _____

Chest: _____

Back Length: _____

Height: _____

Weight: _____

Notes: _____

_____

_____

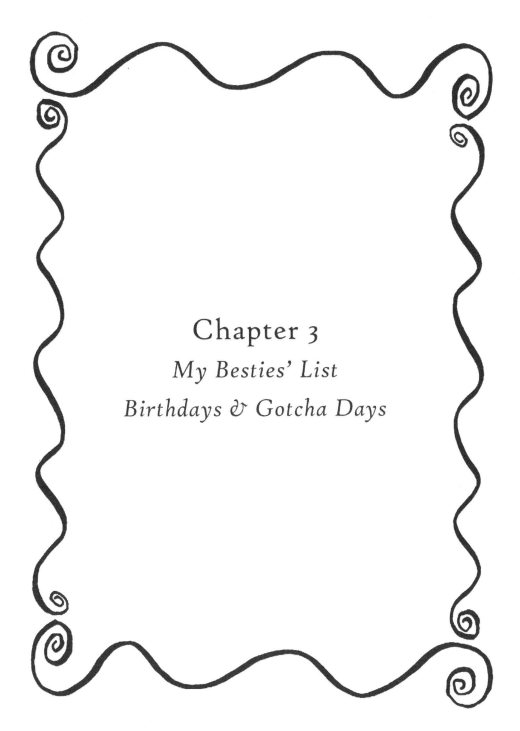

Chapter 3
My Besties' List
Birthdays & Gotcha Days

My Besties List

IG Name	Name(s)	Mom or Dad	Birthday	Gotcha
e.g. Lady.Bouj	Boujee	Louise	5.7.17	12.14.18

_____

_____

_____

_____

_____

_____

_____

_____

_____

_____

_____

IG Name   Name(s)   Mom or Dad   Birthday   Gotcha

IG Name   *Name(s)*   *Mom or Dad*   *Birthday*   *Gotcha*

_____

_____

_____

_____

_____

_____

_____

_____

_____

_____

_____

_____

IG Name	Name(s)	Mom or Dad	Birthday	Gotcha

IG Name   Name(s)   Mom or Dad   Birthday   Gotcha

_____

_____

_____

_____

_____

_____

_____

_____

_____

_____

_____

_____

Chapter 4

My Besties' Page by Page

All About Them

My Besties Page by Page
All About Them

Bestie:

IG Name:

Mom/Dad/:

Other Person:

Family Names:

Birthday:

Gotcha Day:

Measurements:

Favorite Colors:

Hashtags:

Gift Ideas:

Notes:

Bestie: _____

IG Name: _____

Mom/Dad/: _____

Other Person: _____

Family Names: _____

Birthday: _____

Gotcha Day: _____

Measurements: _____

_____

Favorite Colors: _____

Hashtags: _____

_____

_____

Gift Ideas: _____

_____

Notes: _____

Bestie: _____

IG Name: _____

Mom/Dad/: _____

Other Person: _____

Family Names: _____

Birthday: _____

Gotcha Day: _____

Measurements: _____

_____

Favorite Colors: _____

Hashtags: _____

_____

_____

Gift Ideas: _____

_____

Notes: _____

Bestie: _____

IG Name: _____

Mom/Dad/: _____

Other Person: _____

Family Names: _____

Birthday: _____

Gotcha Day: _____

Measurements: _____

_____

Favorite Colors: _____

Hashtags: _____

_____

_____

Gift Ideas: _____

_____

Notes: _____

Bestie: _____

IG Name: _____

Mom/Dad/: _____

Other Person: _____

Family Names: _____

Birthday: _____

Gotcha Day: _____

Measurements: _____

_____

Favorite Colors: _____

Hashtags: _____

_____

_____

Gift Ideas: _____

_____

Notes: _____

Bestie:

IG Name:

Mom/Dad/:

Other Person:

Family Names:

Birthday:

Gotcha Day:

Measurements:

Favorite Colors:

Hashtags:

Gift Ideas:

Notes:

Bestie: _____

IG Name: _____

Mom/Dad/: _____

Other Person: _____

Family Names: _____

Birthday: _____

Gotcha Day: _____

Measurements: _____

_____

Favorite Colors: _____

Hashtags: _____

_____

_____

Gift Ideas: _____

_____

Notes: _____

Bestie: _____

IG Name: _____

Mom/Dad/: _____

Other Person: _____

Family Names: _____

Birthday: _____

Gotcha Day: _____

Measurements: _____

_____

Favorite Colors: _____

Hashtags: _____

_____

_____

Gift Ideas: _____

_____

Notes: _____

Bestie: _____

IG Name: _____

Mom/Dad/: _____

Other Person: _____

Family Names: _____

Birthday: _____

Gotcha Day: _____

Measurements: _____

_____

Favorite Colors: _____

Hashtags: _____

_____

_____

Gift Ideas: _____

_____

Notes: _____

Bestie: _____

IG Name: _____

Mom/Dad/: _____

Other Person: _____

Family Names: _____

Birthday: _____

Gotcha Day: _____

Measurements: _____

_____

Favorite Colors: _____

Hashtags: _____

_____

_____

Gift Ideas: _____

_____

Notes: _____

Bestie: _____

IG Name: _____

Mom/Dad/: _____

Other Person: _____

Family Names: _____

Birthday: _____

Gotcha Day: _____

Measurements: _____

_____

Favorite Colors: _____

Hashtags: _____

_____

_____

Gift Ideas: _____

_____

Notes: _____

Bestie: _____

IG Name: _____

Mom/Dad/: _____

Other Person: _____

Family Names: _____

Birthday: _____

Gotcha Day: _____

Measurements: _____

_____

Favorite Colors: _____

Hashtags: _____

_____

_____

Gift Ideas: _____

_____

Notes: _____

Chapter 5

Weddings & Anniversaries

Romantic Stories

Chapter 5
Weddings & Anniversaries
Romantic Stories

Use this section to record the details and dates of your furiend couples...or maybe for your own wedding?

Here are two romantic stories.

Meet Romeo & Delilah
@romeo_reggie_willow & @delilah_diary

Here is the story of a legendary IG romance! Beautiful international super model Delilah met her prince during a photo shoot at the headquarters of the glittery Swarovski-bejeweled Furdrobe house of dog fashion in England. Romeo was known as the *King* of Kent and he proposed to her right then and there at Furdrobe. Look at @Furdrobe to see the magnificent designs they create.

The wedding took place on September 19, 2020 on the Grand Bandstand in Brighton as suggested by the groom. A few weeks before, the "Bride Tribe" threw a bridal shower and hen party at the Beverly Hills Hotel in Los Angeles.

The Bride Tribe, aka wedding party, included: Boujee (@lady. bouj) as the Maid of Honor and bridesmaids
Cozie (@cozette_warm_and_cozie_tzu)

Lola (@lola_imperial_shihtzu) and Lily (@lily_the_tzu).

Delilah gave them all a full ensemble of Swarovski encrusted bows, ivory beaded necklaces and the famous Furdrobe Fairydust tutus to wear in the wedding.

As you can imagine, Delilah's wedding ballgown was fit for royalty. She wore it beautifully as a tiny princess surrounded by an ocean of Swarovski crystals all designed and created by Rachelle Fawcett, the owner of Furdrobe, lovingly called the Fairydogmother.

It was truly a breath-taking affair to remember as Delilah floated through the town on the way to the ceremony in her horse-drawn carriage to the cheers of all the bystanders lining the streets.

This dreamy event was all captured with the photography of Vasi of @petpix_world.

After the wedding and elegant reception, Romeo swept his bride away to the iconic 14th century Bodiam Castle for their honeymoon.

The groom, a fashion icon himself, says one of the parts he liked the most was talking to Rachelle at Furdrobe and discussing the groom's outfit and what the ushers would wear.

His advice to future grooms: "Have fun, enjoy your stag do, make sure you look your best as you never know when you might get papped by the Paparazzi!"

Romeo describes so many unexpected and delightful wedding gifts received from the wedding party and others, including a beautiful portrait from his bride. They even had a star named in their honor.

The honeymoon was so lovely, he says, "With just the two of us reminiscing about our amazing wedding day and how we would be forever grateful to all our friends who attended from the world over that made it so perfect."

Meet Max & Bella
@max_and_bootie & @babybella_theshihtzu

As told by Bella's Mom:

"Max and Bella always had a thing for each other. He was one of Bella's first IG furiends. They then became Besties, but soon realized they were in love! And so, the romance began. They officially became a couple in 2019. A year later, on their first anniversary, Max sent Bella the most beautiful necklace and asked if she would pawmarry him. Of course, she said yes and so the planning began.

"First to pick a location. Bella wanted a beautiful beach. Santorini, Greece was the perfect place. We set the date for July 1, 2021 at 6pm. Next was choosing a bridal party. Bella chose her sister, Sophie, as her maid of honor.

The flower girl was little Amber @lola_imperial_shihtzu. As her bridesmaids she chose:

Boujee @Lady.Bouj
Taylor @dshawn59
Lola @lola_imperial_shihtzu
Maisy @amaiseballs_theshihtzu
Sadie @sadiecakesdivatzu
Cozie @cozette_warm_and_cozie_tzu."

Bella's exquisite wedding gown and veil were expertly styled and created by her talented mom. The bridesmaids' dresses were also designed and created by the bride's mom. They were pink in a color named Bella Pink because Bella looks so beautiful when she wears it. Each dress was a little different with intricate embellishments and details. The bridesmaid's name was beautifully embroidered inside. The elegant matching bows were made by @sadiecakesdivarzu's Mom.

The Mother of the Bride goes on to say:

"While we were busy planning the wedding, Bella had the most amazing bridesmaids that showered her with gifts and put on the bachelorette party in Las Vegas. The bachelorette party and magnificent wedding would not have been so perfect if we didn't have the help of our furiends celebrating and creating beautiful edits with us. It really was a very special day."

And from the groom's view:

"Max's feelings were that he wanted it to be Bella's dream day. It was his dream to marry Bella. He knew early on Bella was the one for him, but it took them awhile to get together because one or the other was dating somepawdy else when the other was free! I think it was Bella who finally said enough and went IG official with Max as her #mcm (Man Crush Monday), and then on Wednesday Max made her his #wcw (Woman Crush Wednesday), and the rest is history.

"Max started early with 'Happy Wife Happy Life' because he loves Bella and wants her to be happy. That said, a lot of his feelings and wishes for the wedding were pawfectly in-line with Bella's. He wanted it to be a beautiful day so details mattered to him too.

"He bought his groomsmen tuxedos so they would all look the same. He wanted it picture perfect because that matters with an IG wedding. Max and Bella decided the wedding location together. They had their bachelor and bachelorette pawties the same weekend but at different locations.

"Max helped with details like table settings, flowers and dance floor details but let Bella make the final decisions. That is his advice for any grooms to be. Hopefully you are as well matched as Bella and Max, but be supportive to your bride because it is a day she has been dreaming of furever.

"Your dream as a groom will be to marry your girl, but if you have any part of the wedding you feel strongly about (like steak at the reception) speak up. Your bride will want you to be happy too!

" And don't forget the honeymoon!"

Wedding Details & Dates

#Hashtag:

Bride/Groom:

Wedding Date:

Venue:

Parties:

Gift Ideas:

Notes:

#Hashtag:

Bride/Groom:

Wedding Date:

Venue:

Parties:

Gift Ideas:

Notes:

#Hashtag:

Bride/Groom:

Wedding Date:

Venue:

Parties:

Gift Ideas:

Notes:

#Hashtag:

Bride/Groom:

Wedding Date:

Venue:

Parties:

Gift Ideas:

Notes:

#Hashtag: _____

Bride/Groom: _____

Wedding Date: _____

Venue: _____

Parties: _____

Gift Ideas: _____

Notes: _____

#Hashtag: _____

Bride/Groom: _____

Wedding Date: _____

Venue: _____

Parties: _____

Gift Ideas: _____

Notes: _____

#Hashtag: _____

Bride/Groom: _____

Wedding Date: _____

Venue: _____

Parties: _____

Gift Ideas: _____

Notes: _____

_____

#Hashtag: _____

Bride/Groom: _____

Wedding Date: _____

Venue: _____

Parties: _____

Gift Ideas: _____

Notes: _____

#Hashtag:

Bride/Groom:

Wedding Date:

Venue:

Parties:

Gift Ideas:

Notes:

#Hashtag:

Bride/Groom:

Wedding Date:

Venue:

Parties:

Gift Ideas:

Notes:

#Hashtag: _____

Bride/Groom: _____

Wedding Date: _____

Venue: _____

Parties: _____

Gift Ideas: _____

Notes: _____

_____

#Hashtag: _____

Bride/Groom: _____

Wedding Date: _____

Venue: _____

Parties: _____

Gift Ideas: _____

Notes: _____

#Hashtag:

Bride/Groom:

Wedding Date:

Venue:

Parties:

Gift Ideas:

Notes:

#Hashtag:

Bride/Groom:

Wedding Date:

Venue:

Parties:

Gift Ideas:

Notes:

#Hashtag:

Bride/Groom:

Wedding Date:

Venue:

Parties:

Gift Ideas:

Notes:

#Hashtag:

Bride/Groom:

Wedding Date:

Venue:

Parties:

Gift Ideas:

Notes:

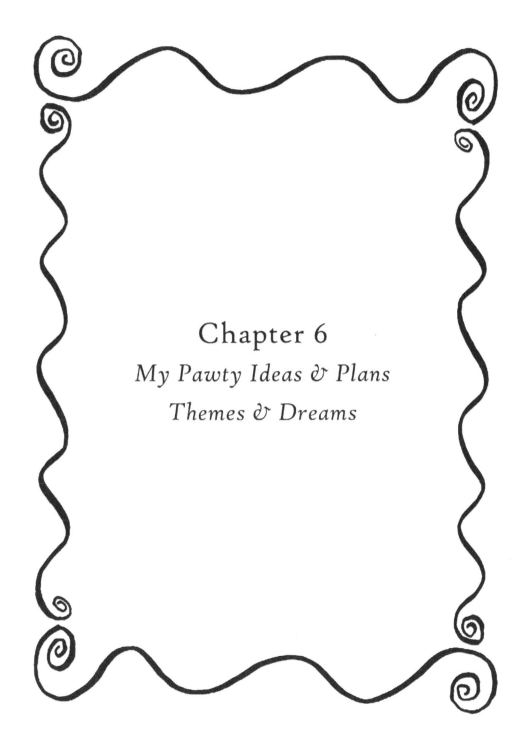

Chapter 6

My Pawty Ideas & Plans

Themes & Dreams

Chapter 6
My Pawty Ideas & Dreams

A fabulous concept came to my attention while I was interviewing dog momagers for the first **Behind the Scenes** book. It answers the question of how to celebrate our fur babies' birthdays, gotcha days and other events without breaking the budget.

Here is the beautiful, heartwarming story of **"The Birthday Puppy"** from Deb, the Founder, and a cheat sheet on the steps of how it can work for you.

"I started **The Birthday Puppy** in 2015 leaving my job as an Interior Designer in my own design studio for 25 years. It started as just an idea. I had 25K followers on our dog Willow's account and would receive Direct Messages from friends who wanted to send her gifts.

"So, knowing that I wanted to start another company, I followed my passion ~ my pups! I also knew I wanted it to have a **philanthropic mission**. I don't do anything small ~ it's all or nothing. So, the year we launched we combined Birthday Boxes, fashion, bakery and giving back to the community.

"We only included the most unusual and high-quality toys you couldn't find elsewhere. We made wearing tutus a necessity! We loved the concept of letting the community give to each other without feeling that they were overwhelmed with cost. For that reason, we have kept the contribution at $6 from day one with the promise that we will never raise the price – so that we can continue to spread joy to as many as possible.

"We do weddings, puppy showers, birthdays, get well, condolences and every occasion in between. And we host Puppy Prom, Halloween and Secret Santa each year.   All events support a charity which the community selects through collaboration. I make all the costumes too!

"We have an Angel Network which I match. Community members give to our fund for others who need cheer, help, or a surprise. **It truly is the best use of social media – spreading joy, celebrating others and helping financially those who need it.**

"We send out about two dozen boxes each week. The way it works is that a community member will notify us of an upcoming birthday or other occasion. We start a DM group of the pup's friends to invite them to join in. The person who starts the group gets their $6 contribution on me as a thank you for their kindness. [Note: a sample of box inclusions follow this story.]

"I continue to search for the best seamstresses who sew for me and make my designs into a reality. We have great bakers and I am always looking for that next fabulous toy.

"It's a great company with a great mission and it fills my heart with joy every day!"

You can contact Deb at The Birthday Puppy by the website or via Instagram:
www.thebirthdaypuppy.com
@thebirthdaypuppy

Here is how it works and a peek at a sample Birthday Box:

Each themed box is filled to the brim customized with goodies for your pet and for you. You can choose from the themes offered on the website or ask for a customized one.

The Princess base box on the website consists of 3 princess types of toys, an accessory such as a crown and a treat. You may also request a specific item you would like to include in the box and add additional items such as a sweater or tutu for a fee.

The Princess Box cost is $60. It would therefore need at least 10 friends to participate at $6 contribution each. Most likely more than 10 friends sign up and then all the incremental dollars go to the charity of choice – The Betty White Foundation for a recent example.

On the website you will find additional gifts, bakery items and very fun "Paw La Carte" items. You can also purchase tickets to the fundraising Prom and Halloween Parade for such great causes as The National Canine Cancer Foundation.

I hope this story might fill your head with new ideas. It filled my heart with delight! Use the following pages for your own party plans & dreams.

Chapter 7
Fun Hashtags, Pawties & Clubs

Fun Hashtags, Pawties & Clubs

A place to write in and remember!

#lucysmonthlypurpleday [last Wednesday of the month]

#tututuesdaywithpoppi

#boujeetribeofficial [third Wednesday of the month]

#EverleighsthisorthatThursdays

#HavensThankfulthursday

#FFRCrownYourWeek [Mondays @fitforroyaltydesigns]

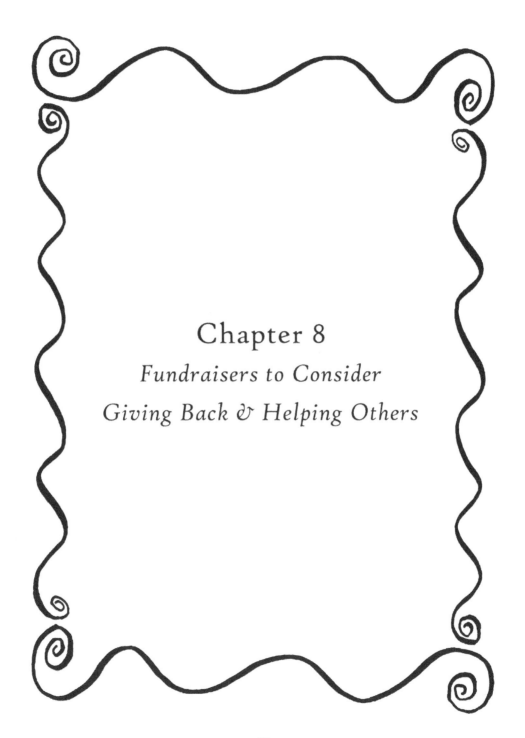

Chapter 8

Fundraisers to Consider
Giving Back & Helping Others

Chapter 8

Fundraisers to Consider ~ Giving Back

& Helping Others

This is arguably one of the best aspects of Instagram and other social media! Use the space in this section to keep track of the causes you wish to support.

Take **@Ginger_doggie** as an example. She uses her platform to support well researched causes. In one instance a raffle was put on to raise funds for **@homewardtrailsrescue** in memory of **@drippingdogig**. $750 was raised for this organization.

"Ginger's Closet" is a permanent fixture in the Green K9 Urbana store. **@Ginger_Doggie** donates all the items. The profits from sales go to great causes. The first $550 went to **@uanimals.official**. This organization helps rescue and feed all animals affected by the war in Ukraine.

An additional $300 from the sale of Ginger's Closet went to Second

Chance Wildlife Center **@2ndchancewc** dedicated to saving Maryland's wildlife.

Another shining example of InstaDogs using their platform for good is lovely Diva from the South of France ~ **@divashihtzu**. One initiative she supports is **@2leggedmaia**. Maia's parents have saved and still save many pups from being euthanized. They provide rescued and abandoned dogs with training, special foods, medicines and much needed love and socialization before finding them their forever homes. What a magnificent thing to do!

Faith **@friendly.faith.the.morkie** shares that there are always opportunities to give back to the community. She recently attended the **@the_cfdda** (Community of Fashion Design Dog Association) charity Prom. Proceeds went to **@petrescuepilots** and the ticket and raffle sales went towards a fund to purchase a van for transporting dogs from high kill shelters to safety. The Prom raised over $4k!

One of the most inspirational accounts we follow is **@glamchisters**. Not only are they uber stylish,, but they support important causes and promote worthwhile fundraisers.

Just read **PetPix World Magazine** for even more ideas and to find a number of rescue organizations to support. Supporting rescue is one of the main thrusts of the publication, in making the world a better place.

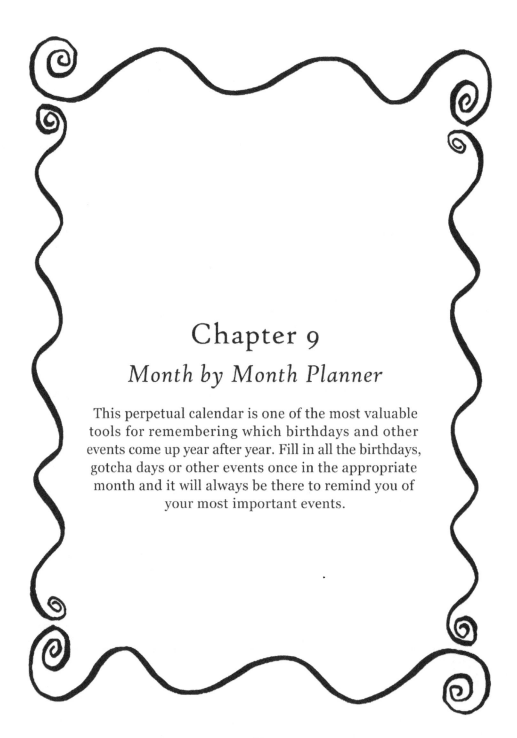

Chapter 9
Month by Month Planner

This perpetual calendar is one of the most valuable tools for remembering which birthdays and other events come up year after year. Fill in all the birthdays, gotcha days or other events once in the appropriate month and it will always be there to remind you of your most important events.

January

1 _____

2 _____

3 _____

4 _____

5 _____

6 _____

7 _____

8 _____

9 _____

10 _____

11 _____

12 _____

13 _____

14 _____

15 _____

16 _____

January

17 _____

18 _____

19 _____

20 _____

21 _____

22 _____

23 _____

24 _____

25 _____

26 _____

27 _____

28 _____

29 _____

30 _____

31 _____

_____

February

1 _____

2 _____

3 _____

4 _____

5 _____

6 _____

7 _____

8 _____

9 _____

10 _____

11 _____

12 _____

13 _____

14 _____

15 _____

16 _____

February

17 _____

18 _____

19 _____

20 _____

21 _____

22 _____

23 _____

24 _____

25 _____

26 _____

27 _____

28 _____

29 _____

_____

_____

_____

March

1 _____

2 _____

3 _____

4 _____

5 _____

6 _____

7 _____

8 _____

9 _____

10 _____

11 _____

12 _____

13 _____

14 _____

15 _____

16 _____

March

17 _____

18 _____

19 _____

20 _____

21 _____

22 _____

23 _____

24 _____

25 _____

26 _____

27 _____

28 _____

29 _____

30 _____

31 _____

_____

April

1 _____

2 _____

3 _____

4 _____

5 _____

6 _____

7 _____

8 _____

9 _____

10 _____

11 _____

12 _____

13 _____

14 _____

15 _____

16 _____

April

17 _____

18 _____

19 _____

20 _____

21 _____

22 _____

23 _____

24 _____

25 _____

26 _____

27 _____

28 _____

29 _____

30 _____

_____

_____

May

1 _____

2 _____

3 _____

4 _____

5 _____

6 _____

7 _____

8 _____

9 _____

10 _____

11 _____

12 _____

13 _____

14 _____

15 _____

16 _____

May

17

18

19

20

21

22

23

24

25

26

27

28

29

30

31

June

1 _____

2 _____

3 _____

4 _____

5 _____

6 _____

7 _____

8 _____

9 _____

10 _____

11 _____

12 _____

13 _____

14 _____

15 _____

16 _____

June

17 _____

18 _____

19 _____

20 _____

21 _____

22 _____

23 _____

24 _____

25 _____

26 _____

27 _____

28 _____

29 _____

30 _____

_____

_____

July

1 _____

2 _____

3 _____

4 _____

5 _____

6 _____

7 _____

8 _____

9 _____

10 _____

11 _____

12 _____

13 _____

14 _____

15 _____

16 _____

July

17

18

19

20

21

22

23

24

25

26

27

28

29

30

31

August

1 _____

2 _____

3 _____

4 _____

5 _____

6 _____

7 _____

8 _____

9 _____

10 _____

11 _____

12 _____

13 _____

14 _____

15 _____

16 _____

August

17 _____

18 _____

19 _____

20 _____

21 _____

22 _____

23 _____

24 _____

25 _____

26 _____

27 _____

28 _____

29 _____

30 _____

31 _____

_____

September

1 _____

2 _____

3 _____

4 _____

5 _____

6 _____

7 _____

8 _____

9 _____

10 _____

11 _____

12 _____

13 _____

14 _____

15 _____

16 _____

September

17 _____

18 _____

19 _____

20 _____

21 _____

22 _____

23 _____

24 _____

25 _____

26 _____

27 _____

28 _____

29 _____

30 _____

_____

_____

October

1 _____

2 _____

3 _____

4 _____

5 _____

6 _____

7 _____

8 _____

9 _____

10 _____

11 _____

12 _____

13 _____

14 _____

15 _____

16 _____

October

17 _____

18 _____

19 _____

20 _____

21 _____

22 _____

23 _____

24 _____

25 _____

26 _____

27 _____

28 _____

29 _____

30 _____

31 _____

_____

November

1 _____

2 _____

3 _____

4 _____

5 _____

6 _____

7 _____

8 _____

9 _____

10 _____

11 _____

12 _____

13 _____

14 _____

15 _____

16 _____

November

17 _____

18 _____

19 _____

20 _____

21 _____

22 _____

23 _____

24 _____

25 _____

26 _____

27 _____

28 _____

29 _____

30 _____

_____

_____

December

1 _____

2 _____

3 _____

4 _____

5 _____

6 _____

7 _____

8 _____

9 _____

10 _____

11 _____

12 _____

13 _____

14 _____

15 _____

16 _____

December

17 _____

18 _____

19 _____

20 _____

21 _____

22 _____

23 _____

24 _____

25 _____

26 _____

27 _____

28 _____

29 _____

30 _____

31 _____

_____

Chapter 10

My Favorites: Designers & Boutiques

Chapter 10

My Favorites: Designers & Boutiques

It is so fun to browse all the items available online for our fur babies! Use these pages to make a note of your favorites and come back when it's time to add to your poochie's wardrobe or to find a gift for a good friend.

There are so many to choose from. Here are the stories of a few of *our* favorites.

KoaBear Bandanas
@koabear_bandanas
www.etsy.com/shop/KoaBearBandanasShop

Tina Timboy, fondly known as Auntie T, is the owner and creator of KoaBear Bandanas and the momager of @koabear_n_honigirl. She lives in Maui and creates the most delightful and extremely well-made things. You can find them on Instagram and her Etsy Shop. I love her story and hope you will too.

*When did KoaBear Bandanas **TM** start?*

"As a hobby, February of 2016. It became a sole proprietorship business with a trademarked name in May of 2016."

*What inspired you to start KoaBear Bandanas **TM**?*

"My Shipoo, KoaBear. He was 4 years old when I started making bandanas for him. I didn't like the tie-on style, so I made the over-the-collar style. It's so hot in Hawaii, but wanted to add a pop of color/fashion to his everyday look."

Did you work before KoaBear Bandanas тм ?

"Yes. I was in accounting for 25 years. I quit my "day job" in May 2016, to focus just on KBB and a stay-at-home mom to my (human) son and KoaBear."

How did it go from a hobby to a business?

"Instagram! I would post pics of KoaBear in his bandanas and people would ask where they could buy them. In the first month, I had given away bandanas to all his Instagram friends. One of those friends loved the over the collar style and placed an order of 10-15 bandanas to give as gifts. Then it spread pretty quickly, through IG and word of mouth."

Do you only make Bandanas?

"No. In (almost) 7 years of being in business, I went from just bandanas to harnesses. Then added coats and hoodies. We rescued a girl dog from South Korea, and that's when I started making dresses. Now I have a Fancy Paws Collection of fancier, sparkly dresses and bow ties. I have also expanded to infant and toddler clothing called KoaBear Kidz."

Where do you see yourself in 5 years?

"I absolutely love what I do and cannot see myself doing anything else. I am living my dream job and creating is my passion. I have become extremely busy and could probably use more help, but I also love being a one-woman business. So, if it gets too overwhelming, I may cut back on items I offer, but for now, I love where I'm at."

Miss Teddy & Young Woofians
@missteddyuk and @young_woofians
www.missteddy.com & www.youngwoofians.com
www.etsy.com/shop/MissTeddyUK

Hailing from Nottingham in the UK, Sue tells the story of her boutiques of exquisitely handmade dog clothing (@missteddyuk) and her unique line of tear stain and other supplies (@young_woofians). She is one amazing lady I have greatly admired over the years. She is the epitome of kindness and positive energy especially on IG. Her pride and joy is her dog, Miss Teddy.

This is what she said:

"I created Miss Teddy, the company, several years ago from pure indulgence really ~ designing & making clothes and selling them all over the world. It was all done from my beautiful Chapel and several staff.

"Miss Teddy had dreadful tear stains and I knew if I could resolve this, I would create a company and help other dogs! Young Woofians was born and we have never looked back!

"It keeps me so busy. I am creating new products all the time and working with the University of Nottinghamshire on my designs: an anti-nibble guard to stop dogs from chewing their feet and a comfy collar that I believe will replace the cone of shame."

Chicka-Bow-Wow-Fashions
@chickabowwowfashions
www.facebook.com/Chicka-Bow-Wow-Fashions
www.etsy.com/shop/ChicaBowWow

Here you will find unusual, fun and inventive pet fashion couture! CBW was born of artist Sandra Barnes' desire to clothe her own fur kids in edgy fashions 15 years ago and she is still at it.

We love that she re-purposes, upcycles and uses vintage items when possible. All of her denim items are re-purposed. Many of her styles are One of a Kind or Limited Edition, using elements of designer human clothing, vintage yardage, trim and jewelry. Each piece is individually designed and hand sewn.

As an artist, Sandra's favorite part of the process is the design, but she loves sewing too. She tells us, "There is something decidedly unique incorporated into each piece, be it antique lace, a fabulous vintage brooch or the sumptuous fabric of a former Chanel suit. Sometimes a client will send an article of their own clothing that may be out of fashion, no longer fits, or has been ruined by a stain or tear. Repurposing breathes new life into their clothing with significant meaning and memories."

She goes on to explain, "Fashion is ephemeral, while fabric and pollution are not. After all of the inspiration, image-making, and excitement passes, the clothing remains in wardrobes everywhere.

"After its origins on the farm, forest or oil field, those articles spent some time morphing into their present form. Eco-savvy dog fashions mean not only reducing post-consumer refuse, but also pre-consumer waste and pollution. It is my pleasure to re-purpose them into a treasure that will be worn and cherished for years to come."

Pawz Dog Hoodies & Harnesses
@pawz_hoodies
www.pawzhoodies.com

We could not complete this section without a huge shout out to Leann of Pawz Hoodies. Without fail, her designs are not only fine-looking but exceptionally well made. Her harnesses are super safe, easy to use and a favorite staple of my dog's wardrobe. If you do not own one yet – it is highly recommended!

The story on her website was written by a fan of hers and it goes like this:

"PAWZ was born in the small city of Kelowna in Western Canada. Leann, the founder of PAWZ and designer of every one of its products, is not what you would consider to be the prototypical entrepreneur. She says, 'To be honest, I don't really know what being an entrepreneur means!'

"Leann is incredibly humble about her designs, her quality and her business as a whole. She makes other Canadians, usually known for being nice and often self-deprecating, look like egocentric braggarts!

"An abstract artist in her younger years, Leann would never sign or even acknowledge her own work, preferring to avoid the limelight. Even today she prefers to allow her products to speak for themselves.

"Over the years she has purchased numerous articles of clothing for her fur babies. As she continued to buy items online, she was repeatedly let down by the quality of the products she received. Until one day she decided to create the clothes for her dogs herself and so Pawz Hoodies was born."

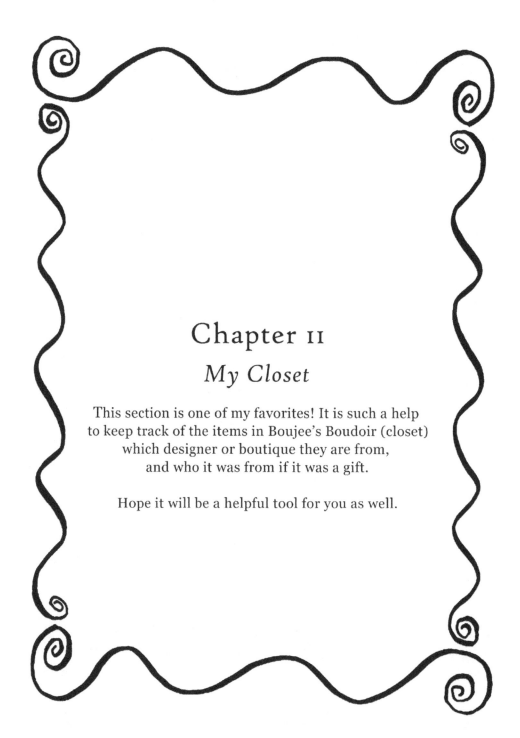

Chapter 11
My Closet

This section is one of my favorites! It is such a help
to keep track of the items in Boujee's Boudoir (closet)
which designer or boutique they are from,
and who it was from if it was a gift.

Hope it will be a helpful tool for you as well.

Item	Designer/Shop	Gift From?	Date

Item	Designer/Shop	Gift From?	Date

Item	Designer/Shop	Gift From?	Date

Item	Designer/Shop	Gift From?	Date

Item	Designer/Shop	Gift From?	Date

Item	Designer/Shop	Gift From?	Date

Item	Designer/Shop	Gift From?	Date

Item	Designer/Shop	Gift From?	Date

Item	Designer/Shop	Gift From?	Date

Item	Designer/Shop	Gift From?	Date

Item	Designer/Shop	Gift From?	Date

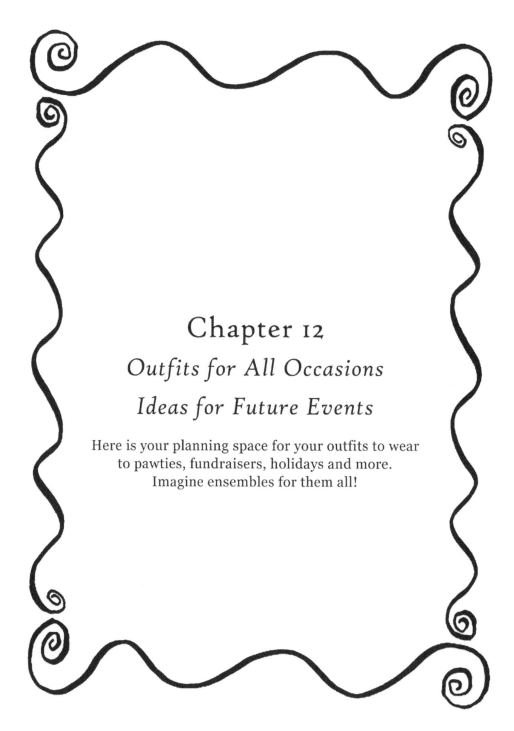

Chapter 12

Outfits for All Occasions

Ideas for Future Events

Here is your planning space for your outfits to wear
to pawties, fundraisers, holidays and more.
Imagine ensembles for them all!

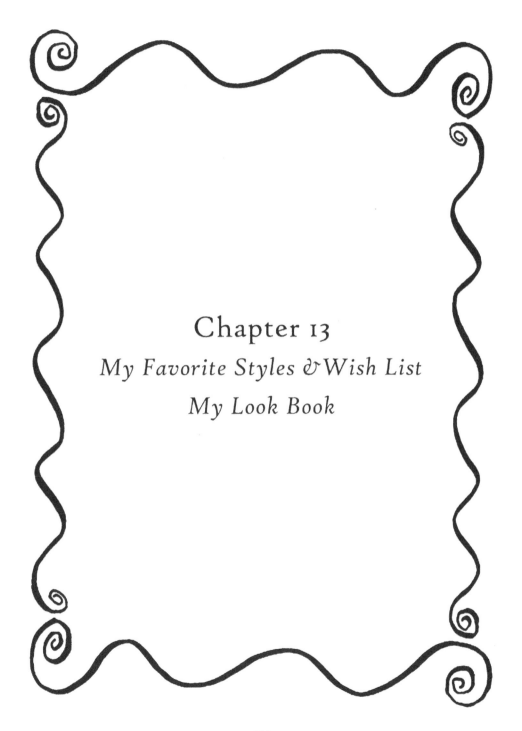

Chapter 13
My Favorite Styles & Wish List

My Look Book

Wish List

e.g.   Step In Confetti Harness by Pawz Hoodies

e.g.   Fit For Royalty cuff

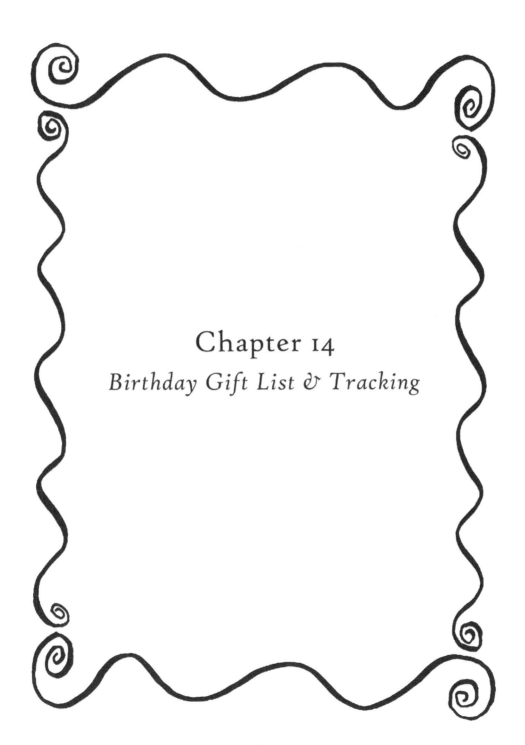

Chapter 14
Birthday Gift List & Tracking

Birthday Gift List & Tracking

Name	Gift	Sent	Rec'd	Date	Thank'd	Post'd
Cozie	Miss Teddy Collar	N	Y	5/7/20	Y	Y

Name	Gift	Sent	Rec'd	Date	Thank'd	Post'd

Name	Gift	Sent	Rec'd	Date	Thank'd	Post'd

Name	Gift	Sent	Rec'd	Date	Thank'd	Post'd

Name	Gift	Sent	Rec'd	Date	Thank'd	Post'd

Name	Gift	Sent	Rec'd	Date	Thank'd	Post'd

Name	Gift	Sent	Rec'd	Date	Thank'd	Post'd

Chapter 15
Holiday Gift List & Tracking

Holiday Gift List & Tracking

Name	Gift	Sent	Rec'd	Date	Thank'd	Post'd
Zeva	CBW dress	N	Y	12/15/21	Y	Y

Name	Gift	Sent	Rec'd	Date	Thank'd	Post'd

Name	Gift	Sent	Rec'd	Date	Thank'd	Post'd

Name	Gift	Sent	Rec'd	Date	Thank'd	Post'd

Name	Gift	Sent	Rec'd	Date	Thank'd	Post'd

Name	Gift	Sent	Rec'd	Date	Thank'd	Post'd

Name	Gift	Sent	Rec'd	Date	Thank'd	Post'd

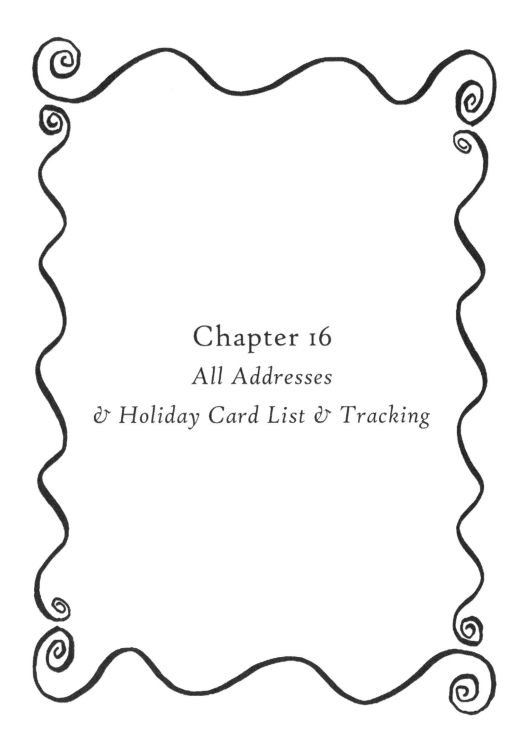

Chapter 16

All Addresses

& Holiday Card List & Tracking

All Addresses
& Holiday Card List & Tracking

Use this section however you wish, year by year. Some accounts just type in the return addresses of their friends so they will all be in one place. Some prefer to write entries with their special purple ink and fountain pen. Refer to this list for your friends' addresses for other occasion gifts, too. If you prefer a digital version, please see the Book Bonus section on how to download your free gift of your pup's very own address book data base!

Friend Name: _____ Sent __ Rec'd __ Year ____

IG Name: _____ Parent: _____

Address: _____

_____

Friend Name: _____ Sent __ Rec'd __ Year ____

IG Name: _____ Parent: _____

Address: _____

_____

Friend Name: _____ Sent __ Rec'd __ Year ____

IG Name: _____ Parent: _____

Address: _____

_____

Friend Name: _____ Sent __ Rec'd __ Year ____

IG Name: _____ Parent: _____

Address: _____

_____

Friend Name: _____ Sent ___ Rec'd ___ Year ____

IG Name: _____ Parent: _____

Address: _____

_____

Friend Name: _____ Sent ___ Rec'd ___ Year ____

IG Name: _____ Parent: _____

Address: _____

_____

Friend Name: _____ Sent ___ Rec'd ___ Year ____

IG Name: _____ Parent: _____

Address: _____

_____

Friend Name: _____ Sent ___ Rec'd ___ Year ____

IG Name: _____ Parent: _____

Address: _____

_____

Friend Name: _____ Sent ___ Rec'd ___ Year ____

IG Name: _____ Parent: _____

Address: _____

_____

Friend Name: _____ Sent ___ Rec'd ___ Year ____

IG Name: _____ Parent: _____

Address: _____

_____

Friend Name: _____ Sent ___ Rec'd ___ Year ____

IG Name: _____ Parent: _____

Address: _____

_____

Friend Name: _____ Sent ___ Rec'd ___ Year ____

IG Name: _____ Parent: _____

Address: _____

_____

Friend Name: _____ Sent ___ Rec'd ___ Year ____

IG Name: _____ Parent: _____

Address: _____

_____

Friend Name: _____ Sent ___ Rec'd ___ Year ____

IG Name: _____ Parent: _____

Address: _____

_____

Friend Name: _____ Sent ___ Rec'd ___ Year ____

IG Name: _____ Parent: _____

Address: _____

_____

Friend Name: _____ Sent ___ Rec'd ___ Year ____

IG Name: _____ Parent: _____

Address: _____

_____

Friend Name: _____ Sent ___ Rec'd ___ Year ____

IG Name: _____ Parent: _____

Address: _____

_____

Friend Name: _____ Sent ___ Rec'd ___ Year ____

IG Name: _____ Parent: _____

Address: _____

_____

Friend Name: _____ Sent ___ Rec'd ___ Year ____

IG Name: _____ Parent: _____

Address: _____

_____

Friend Name: _____ Sent ___ Rec'd ___ Year ____

IG Name: _____ Parent: _____

Address: _____

_____

Friend Name: _____ Sent ___ Rec'd ___ Year ____

IG Name: _____ Parent: _____

Address: _____

_____

Friend Name: _____ Sent ___ Rec'd ___ Year ____

IG Name: _____ Parent: _____

Address: _____

_____

Friend Name: _____ Sent ___ Rec'd ___ Year ____

IG Name: _____ Parent: _____

Address: _____

_____

Friend Name: _____ Sent ___ Rec'd ___ Year ____

IG Name: _____ Parent: _____

Address: _____

_____

Friend Name: _____ Sent __ Rec'd __ Year ____

IG Name: _____ Parent: _____

Address: _____

_____

Friend Name: _____ Sent __ Rec'd __ Year ____

IG Name: _____ Parent: _____

Address: _____

_____

Friend Name: _____ Sent __ Rec'd __ Year ____

IG Name: _____ Parent: _____

Address: _____

_____

Friend Name: _____ Sent __ Rec'd __ Year ____

IG Name: _____ Parent: _____

Address: _____

_____

Friend Name: _____ Sent __ Rec'd __ Year ____

IG Name: _____ Parent: _____

Address: _____

_____

Friend Name: _____ Sent ___ Rec'd ___ Year ____

IG Name: _____ Parent: _____

Address: _____

_____

Friend Name: _____ Sent ___ Rec'd ___ Year ____

IG Name: _____ Parent: _____

Address: _____

_____

Friend Name: _____ Sent ___ Rec'd ___ Year ____

IG Name: _____ Parent: _____

Address: _____

_____

Friend Name: _____ Sent ___ Rec'd ___ Year ____

IG Name: _____ Parent: _____

Address: _____

_____

Friend Name: _____ Sent ___ Rec'd ___ Year ____

IG Name: _____ Parent: _____

Address: _____

_____

Friend Name: _____ Sent ___ Rec'd ___ Year ____
IG Name: _____ Parent: _____
Address: _____
_____

Friend Name: _____ Sent ___ Rec'd ___ Year ____
IG Name: _____ Parent: _____
Address: _____
_____

Friend Name: _____ Sent ___ Rec'd ___ Year ____
IG Name: _____ Parent: _____
Address: _____
_____

Friend Name: _____ Sent ___ Rec'd ___ Year ____
IG Name: _____ Parent: _____
Address: _____
_____

Friend Name: _____ Sent ___ Rec'd ___ Year ____
IG Name: _____ Parent: _____
Address: _____
_____

Friend Name: _____ Sent __ Rec'd __ Year ____
IG Name: _____ Parent: _____
Address: _____
_____

Friend Name: _____ Sent __ Rec'd __ Year ____
IG Name: _____ Parent: _____
Address: _____
_____

Friend Name: _____ Sent __ Rec'd __ Year ____
IG Name: _____ Parent: _____
Address: _____
_____

Friend Name: _____ Sent __ Rec'd __ Year ____
IG Name: _____ Parent: _____
Address: _____
_____

Friend Name: _____ Sent __ Rec'd __ Year ____
IG Name: _____ Parent: _____
Address: _____
_____

Friend Name: _____ Sent __ Rec'd __ Year ___
IG Name: _____ Parent: _____
Address: _____
_____

Friend Name: _____ Sent __ Rec'd __ Year ___
IG Name: _____ Parent: _____
Address: _____
_____

Friend Name: _____ Sent __ Rec'd __ Year ___
IG Name: _____ Parent: _____
Address: _____
_____

Friend Name: _____ Sent __ Rec'd __ Year ___
IG Name: _____ Parent: _____
Address: _____
_____

Friend Name: _____ Sent __ Rec'd __ Year ___
IG Name: _____ Parent: _____
Address: _____
_____

Friend Name: _____ Sent __ Rec'd __ Year ___

IG Name: _____ Parent: _____

Address: _____

_____

Friend Name: _____ Sent __ Rec'd __ Year ___

IG Name: _____ Parent: _____

Address: _____

_____

Friend Name: _____ Sent __ Rec'd __ Year ___

IG Name: _____ Parent: _____

Address: _____

_____

Friend Name: _____ Sent __ Rec'd __ Year ___

IG Name: _____ Parent: _____

Address: _____

_____

Friend Name: _____ Sent __ Rec'd __ Year ___

IG Name: _____ Parent: _____

Address: _____

_____

Friend Name: _____ Sent ___ Rec'd ___ Year ____
IG Name: _____ Parent: _____
Address: _____
_____

Friend Name: _____ Sent ___ Rec'd ___ Year ____
IG Name: _____ Parent: _____
Address: _____
_____

Friend Name: _____ Sent ___ Rec'd ___ Year ____
IG Name: _____ Parent: _____
Address: _____
_____

Friend Name: _____ Sent ___ Rec'd ___ Year ____
IG Name: _____ Parent: _____
Address: _____
_____

Friend Name: _____ Sent ___ Rec'd ___ Year ____
IG Name: _____ Parent: _____
Address: _____
_____

Friend Name: _____ Sent __ Rec'd __ Year ____
IG Name: _____ Parent: _____
Address: _____
_____

Friend Name: _____ Sent __ Rec'd __ Year ____
IG Name: _____ Parent: _____
Address: _____
_____

Friend Name: _____ Sent __ Rec'd __ Year ____
IG Name: _____ Parent: _____
Address: _____
_____

Friend Name: _____ Sent __ Rec'd __ Year ____
IG Name: _____ Parent: _____
Address: _____
_____

Friend Name: _____ Sent __ Rec'd __ Year ____
IG Name: _____ Parent: _____
Address: _____
_____

Friend Name: _____ Sent __ Rec'd __ Year ___
IG Name: _____ Parent: _____
Address: _____
_____

Friend Name: _____ Sent __ Rec'd __ Year ___
IG Name: _____ Parent: _____
Address: _____
_____

Friend Name: _____ Sent __ Rec'd __ Year ___
IG Name: _____ Parent: _____
Address: _____
_____

Friend Name: _____ Sent __ Rec'd __ Year ___
IG Name: _____ Parent: _____
Address: _____
_____

Friend Name: _____ Sent __ Rec'd __ Year ___
IG Name: _____ Parent: _____
Address: _____
_____

Friend Name: _____ Sent __ Rec'd __ Year ____

IG Name: _____ Parent: _____

Address: _____

_____

Friend Name: _____ Sent __ Rec'd __ Year ____

IG Name: _____ Parent: _____

Address: _____

_____

Friend Name: _____ Sent __ Rec'd __ Year ____

IG Name: _____ Parent: _____

Address: _____

_____

Friend Name: _____ Sent __ Rec'd __ Year ____

IG Name: _____ Parent: _____

Address: _____

_____

Friend Name: _____ Sent __ Rec'd __ Year ____

IG Name: _____ Parent: _____

Address: _____

_____

Friend Name: _____ Sent ___ Rec'd ___ Year ____

IG Name: _____ Parent: _____

Address: _____

_____

Friend Name: _____ Sent ___ Rec'd ___ Year ____

IG Name: _____ Parent: _____

Address: _____

_____

Friend Name: _____ Sent ___ Rec'd ___ Year ____

IG Name: _____ Parent: _____

Address: _____

_____

Friend Name: _____ Sent ___ Rec'd ___ Year ____

IG Name: _____ Parent: _____

Address: _____

_____

Friend Name: _____ Sent ___ Rec'd ___ Year ____

IG Name: _____ Parent: _____

Address: _____

_____

Friend Name: _____ Sent ___ Rec'd ___ Year ____

IG Name: _____ Parent: _____

Address: _____

_____

Friend Name: _____ Sent ___ Rec'd ___ Year ____

IG Name: _____ Parent: _____

Address: _____

_____

Friend Name: _____ Sent ___ Rec'd ___ Year ____

IG Name: _____ Parent: _____

Address: _____

_____

Friend Name: _____ Sent ___ Rec'd ___ Year ____

IG Name: _____ Parent: _____

Address: _____

_____

Friend Name: _____ Sent ___ Rec'd ___ Year ____

IG Name: _____ Parent: _____

Address: _____

_____

Friend Name: _____ Sent __ Rec'd __ Year ___

IG Name: _____ Parent: _____

Address: _____

_____

Friend Name: _____ Sent __ Rec'd __ Year ___

IG Name: _____ Parent: _____

Address: _____

_____

Friend Name: _____ Sent __ Rec'd __ Year ___

IG Name: _____ Parent: _____

Address: _____

_____

Friend Name: _____ Sent __ Rec'd __ Year ___

IG Name: _____ Parent: _____

Address: _____

_____

Friend Name: _____ Sent __ Rec'd __ Year ___

IG Name: _____ Parent: _____

Address: _____

_____

Friend Name: _____ Sent __ Rec'd __ Year ____

IG Name: _____ Parent: _____

Address: _____

_____

Friend Name: _____ Sent __ Rec'd __ Year ____

IG Name: _____ Parent: _____

Address: _____

_____

Friend Name: _____ Sent __ Rec'd __ Year ____

IG Name: _____ Parent: _____

Address: _____

_____

Friend Name: _____ Sent __ Rec'd __ Year ____

IG Name: _____ Parent: _____

Address: _____

_____

Friend Name: _____ Sent __ Rec'd __ Year ____

IG Name: _____ Parent: _____

Address: _____

_____

Friend Name: _____ Sent __ Rec'd __ Year ____

IG Name: _____ Parent: _____

Address: _____

_____

Friend Name: _____ Sent __ Rec'd __ Year ____

IG Name: _____ Parent: _____

Address: _____

_____

Friend Name: _____ Sent __ Rec'd __ Year ____

IG Name: _____ Parent: _____

Address: _____

_____

Friend Name: _____ Sent __ Rec'd __ Year ____

IG Name: _____ Parent: _____

Address: _____

_____

Friend Name: _____ Sent __ Rec'd __ Year ____

IG Name: _____ Parent: _____

Address: _____

_____

Friend Name: _____ Sent __ Rec'd __ Year ____

IG Name: _____ Parent: _____

Address: _____

_____

Friend Name: _____ Sent __ Rec'd __ Year ____

IG Name: _____ Parent: _____

Address: _____

_____

Friend Name: _____ Sent __ Rec'd __ Year ____

IG Name: _____ Parent: _____

Address: _____

_____

Friend Name: _____ Sent __ Rec'd __ Year ____

IG Name: _____ Parent: _____

Address: _____

_____

Friend Name: _____ Sent __ Rec'd __ Year ____

IG Name: _____ Parent: _____

Address: _____

_____

Friend Name: _____ Sent __ Rec'd __ Year ___
IG Name: _____ Parent: _____
Address: _____
_____

Friend Name: _____ Sent __ Rec'd __ Year ___
IG Name: _____ Parent: _____
Address: _____
_____

Friend Name: _____ Sent __ Rec'd __ Year ___
IG Name: _____ Parent: _____
Address: _____
_____

Friend Name: _____ Sent __ Rec'd __ Year ___
IG Name: _____ Parent: _____
Address: _____
_____

Friend Name: _____ Sent __ Rec'd __ Year ___
IG Name: _____ Parent: _____
Address: _____
_____

Friend Name: _____ Sent ___ Rec'd ___ Year ____

IG Name: _____ Parent: _____

Address: _____

_____

Friend Name: _____ Sent ___ Rec'd ___ Year ____

IG Name: _____ Parent: _____

Address: _____

_____

Friend Name: _____ Sent ___ Rec'd ___ Year ____

IG Name: _____ Parent: _____

Address: _____

_____

Friend Name: _____ Sent ___ Rec'd ___ Year ____

IG Name: _____ Parent: _____

Address: _____

_____

Friend Name: _____ Sent ___ Rec'd ___ Year ____

IG Name: _____ Parent: _____

Address: _____

_____

Friend Name: _____ Sent ___ Rec'd ___ Year ____

IG Name: _____ Parent: _____

Address: _____

_____

Friend Name: _____ Sent ___ Rec'd ___ Year ____

IG Name: _____ Parent: _____

Address: _____

_____

Friend Name: _____ Sent ___ Rec'd ___ Year ____

IG Name: _____ Parent: _____

Address: _____

_____

Friend Name: _____ Sent ___ Rec'd ___ Year ____

IG Name: _____ Parent: _____

Address: _____

_____

Friend Name: _____ Sent ___ Rec'd ___ Year ____

IG Name: _____ Parent: _____

Address: _____

_____

Friend Name: _____ Sent ___ Rec'd ___ Year ____
IG Name: _____ Parent: _____
Address: _____
_____

Friend Name: _____ Sent ___ Rec'd ___ Year ____
IG Name: _____ Parent: _____
Address: _____
_____

Friend Name: _____ Sent ___ Rec'd ___ Year ____
IG Name: _____ Parent: _____
Address: _____
_____

Friend Name: _____ Sent ___ Rec'd ___ Year ____
IG Name: _____ Parent: _____
Address: _____
_____

Friend Name: _____ Sent ___ Rec'd ___ Year ____
IG Name: _____ Parent: _____
Address: _____
_____

Friend Name: _____ Sent __ Rec'd __ Year ___

IG Name: _____ Parent: _____

Address: _____

_____

Friend Name: _____ Sent __ Rec'd __ Year ___

IG Name: _____ Parent: _____

Address: _____

_____

Friend Name: _____ Sent __ Rec'd __ Year ___

IG Name: _____ Parent: _____

Address: _____

_____

Friend Name: _____ Sent __ Rec'd __ Year ___

IG Name: _____ Parent: _____

Address: _____

_____

Friend Name: _____ Sent __ Rec'd __ Year ___

IG Name: _____ Parent: _____

Address: _____

_____

Friend Name: _____ Sent ___ Rec'd ___ Year ____

IG Name: _____ Parent: _____

Address: _____

_____

Friend Name: _____ Sent ___ Rec'd ___ Year ____

IG Name: _____ Parent: _____

Address: _____

_____

Friend Name: _____ Sent ___ Rec'd ___ Year ____

IG Name: _____ Parent: _____

Address: _____

_____

Friend Name: _____ Sent ___ Rec'd ___ Year ____

IG Name: _____ Parent: _____

Address: _____

_____

Friend Name: _____ Sent ___ Rec'd ___ Year ____

IG Name: _____ Parent: _____

Address: _____

_____

Friend Name: _____ Sent __ Rec'd __ Year ____

IG Name: _____ Parent: _____

Address: _____

_____

Friend Name: _____ Sent __ Rec'd __ Year ____

IG Name: _____ Parent: _____

Address: _____

_____

Friend Name: _____ Sent __ Rec'd __ Year ____

IG Name: _____ Parent: _____

Address: _____

_____

Friend Name: _____ Sent __ Rec'd __ Year ____

IG Name: _____ Parent: _____

Address: _____

_____

Friend Name: _____ Sent __ Rec'd __ Year ____

IG Name: _____ Parent: _____

Address: _____

_____

Friend Name: _____ Sent __ Rec'd __ Year ____

IG Name: _____ Parent: _____

Address: _____

_____

Friend Name: _____ Sent __ Rec'd __ Year ____

IG Name: _____ Parent: _____

Address: _____

_____

Friend Name: _____ Sent __ Rec'd __ Year ____

IG Name: _____ Parent: _____

Address: _____

_____

Friend Name: _____ Sent __ Rec'd __ Year ____

IG Name: _____ Parent: _____

Address: _____

_____

Friend Name: _____ Sent __ Rec'd __ Year ____

IG Name: _____ Parent: _____

Address: _____

_____

Friend Name: _____ Sent ___ Rec'd ___ Year ____

IG Name: _____ Parent: _____

Address: _____

_____

Friend Name: _____ Sent ___ Rec'd ___ Year ____

IG Name: _____ Parent: _____

Address: _____

_____

Friend Name: _____ Sent ___ Rec'd ___ Year ____

IG Name: _____ Parent: _____

Address: _____

_____

Friend Name: _____ Sent ___ Rec'd ___ Year ____

IG Name: _____ Parent: _____

Address: _____

_____

Friend Name: _____ Sent ___ Rec'd ___ Year ____

IG Name: _____ Parent: _____

Address: _____

_____

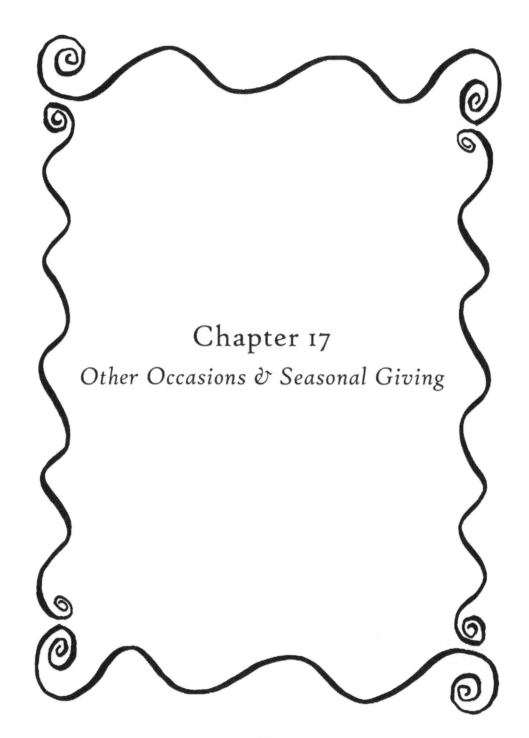

Chapter 17
Other Occasions & Seasonal Giving

Other Occasions & Seasonal Giving

Event	Item	Who	Sent	Rec'd	Date	Thank'd	Post'd

Event	Item	Who	Sent	Rec'd	Date	Thank'd	Post'd

Event	Item	Who	Sent	Rec'd	Date	Thank'd	Post'd

Event	Item	Who	Sent	Rec'd	Date	Thank'd	Post'd

Event	Item	Who	Sent	Rec'd	Date	Thank'd	Post'd

Event	Item	Who	Sent	Rec'd	Date	Thank'd	Post'd

Chapter 18

Gift Ideas & Gifts to Make

Chapter 18
Gift Ideas & Gifts to Make

Here is where you can dream up ideas of what to give your Besties for their next birthday or the holidays. We have included a few unique gifts we love. You'll also find a couple of budget-friendly gifts to make. Enjoy!

Poochie Parfum
@poochieparfum
Poochie Parfum is a perfume for dogs available in two scents: Champagne Kisses & Chic Beach.

Champagne Kisses is a delicate, elegantly classic scent harmonized with soft florals and vanilla. Perfect for the distinguished pooch, it has subtle peony top notes blended with sweet rose and followed by vanilla base notes.

Chic Beach has a light refreshing aquatic scent for the lively, spirited and joyful pooch. The citrus top notes are blended with green leaves and followed by patchouli base notes.

The talented founder, Lori-Rose tells us Poochie Parfum was born out of the unconditional love she has for her fur baby that burst into her life and stole her heart, **Miss Dior (@iammissdior_)** the

InstaFamous Teacup Maltese.

Of course, Dior was named after the beauty and couture house so it is not a surprise that a fragrance was created in her honor.

Dior's mummy explains, "As a pup, Dior would snuggle against me, my fragrance rubbing off onto her coat. I loved to smell her and would spray her with a water-based spritz I made from essential oils for her. I would regularly hear comments on how pretty she smelt."

Lori-Rose had a background in public relations for the beauty and fragrance sector which helped her develop her spritz into a fragrance she could retail for others to enjoy on their fur babies. She emphasizes that Poochie Parfum is made using essential oils and fine fragrances blended with all natural ingredients – "no nasties" and is not tested on animals. It is vegan friendly, kind to nature, Australian made and contains no alcohol.

You can find it in boutique dog stores in Australia and online via DM on Instagram.

Jolifox
@Jolifox_art
myjolifox.bigcartel.com

Jolifox, formerly an illustrator of children's books, is a freelance illustrator in France who can create a joyful portrait of your pet. She had loved looking at the dogs on Instagram, and drew a few portraits just for fun, posting them on her feed.

These very cute interpretations with large eyes quickly became popular with many reaching out to ask for a portrait of their fur baby. They make a unique gift for sure.

This is how it works:
Send in a few of your favorite photos of your pet, and you will receive the portrait by email in a few days or a couple weeks. You can then post it on your social networks or print out a copy for yourself.

You can see samples of her whimsical creations on her Instagram account.
To order and for details, go to **myjolifox.bigcartel.com.**

Some other ideas:

1. **Go to @thebirthdaypuppy or www.thebirthdaypuppy.com** as suggested in Chapter 6 for a delightful, fun, budget-friendly way to celebrate your furiend's birthday or other occasion....and it will give back to a good cause at the same time!

2. Consider honoring a bestie by a gift certificate from **DOGUE Magazine** which they can use for a Cover edit. **@coverdogs** (Especially good for avoiding sometimes costly international shipping).

3. Look up **@crownandpaw** for some fun ideas and custom pet art with a bonus ~ worldwide shipping with a portion of your

purchase toward animal rescue initiatives. They have 220K followers and have donated over $100k to date to this important cause. See #**crownandpawportrait** for examples of their pet art.

4. A wide variety of holiday ornaments personalized with your pet can be found on **Etsy.com**, as well as fun customized pet pillows and a million other things.

And some ideas of gifts to make:

1. Look on **YouTube** for easy tutorials on how to make dog hairbows and collar bows. These are especially meaningful if made of upcycled fabrics.

2. Perhaps you have a favorite treat recipe to make up, package prettily and send along with the recipe to some of your best friends.

3. Knit a soft dog blanket! Instructions and materials available at Michaels and other craft stores.

Use these pages to list ideas of your own:

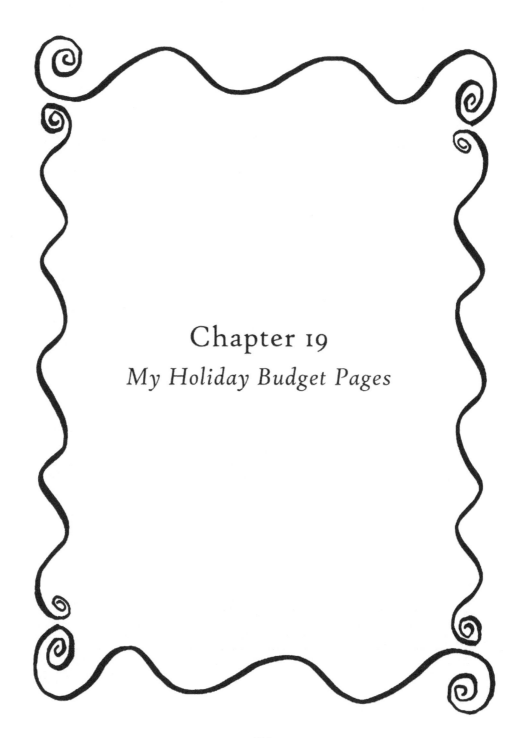

Chapter 19
My Holiday Budget Pages

Chapter 19

My Holiday Budget Pages

Draw up a budget each year and keep track here!

Year:

Holiday Cards

Number Needed:

Budget for Cards: Actual:

Budget for Postage: Actual:

Total Cards: Actual:

Holiday Gifts

Number Needed: Actual:

Budget for Gifts: Actual:

Budget for Wrap: Actual:

Budget for Postage: Actual:

Total Gifts: Actual:

Year:

Holiday Cards

Number Needed:

Budget for Cards: Actual:

Budget for Postage: Actual:

Total Cards: Actual:

Holiday Gifts

Number Needed: Actual:

Budget for Gifts: Actual:

Budget for Wrap: Actual:

Budget for Postage: Actual:

Total Gifts: Actual:

Notes:

Year:

Holiday Cards

Number Needed:

Budget for Cards: Actual:

Budget for Postage: Actual:

Total Cards: Actual:

Holiday Gifts

Number Needed: Actual:

Budget for Gifts: Actual:

Budget for Wrap: Actual:

Budget for Postage: Actual:

Total Gifts: Actual:

Notes:

Year:

Holiday Cards

Number Needed:

Budget for Cards: Actual:

Budget for Postage: Actual:

Total Cards: Actual:

Holiday Gifts

Number Needed: Actual:

Budget for Gifts: Actual:

Budget for Wrap: Actual:

Budget for Postage: Actual:

Total Gifts: Actual:

Notes:

Year:

Holiday Cards

Number Needed:

Budget for Cards: Actual:

Budget for Postage: Actual:

Total Cards: Actual:

Holiday Gifts

Number Needed: Actual:

Budget for Gifts: Actual:

Budget for Wrap: Actual:

Budget for Postage: Actual:

Total Gifts: Actual:

Notes:

Year:

Holiday Cards

Number Needed:

Budget for Cards: Actual:

Budget for Postage: Actual:

Total Cards: Actual:

Holiday Gifts

Number Needed: Actual:

Budget for Gifts: Actual:

Budget for Wrap: Actual:

Budget for Postage: Actual:

Total Gifts: Actual:

Notes:

Year:

Holiday Cards

Number Needed:

Budget for Cards: Actual:

Budget for Postage: Actual:

Total Cards: Actual:

Holiday Gifts

Number Needed: Actual:

Budget for Gifts: Actual:

Budget for Wrap: Actual:

Budget for Postage: Actual:

Total Gifts: Actual:

Notes:

Year:

Holiday Cards

Number Needed:

Budget for Cards: Actual:

Budget for Postage: Actual:

Total Cards: Actual:

Holiday Gifts

Number Needed: Actual:

Budget for Gifts: Actual:

Budget for Wrap: Actual:

Budget for Postage: Actual:

Total Gifts: Actual:

Notes:

Chapter 20

Inspiration ~
Books, Blogs, & Magazines

Chapter 20

Inspiration ~ Books, Blogs & Magazines

Use the space in this section to list your favorites & some to try. Here are some of ours:

I – MAGAZINES

PetPix World Magazine
@petpix_world
www.petpixworld.com

This magazine is yet another success of the vivacious and talented Vasilena, photographer of Vasi Studio fame, in Palm Beach Gardens, Florida! In addition to her studio, she founded PetPix Academy for classes, workshops and a community of members who share their experience and the latest trends.

Pet Pix World Magazine:

- First hybrid pet magazine (digital with videos & print)
- Global reach & diverse for all things pet-related
- Supports pet rescue organizations & fundraisers
- Social media teaching platform

Each issue has a different theme, averages 100-150 pages and is chock full of articles on:

- Upcoming events – virtual and physical
- Pet wellness tips & recipes
- Education on social media
- Pet fashions & designers
- Experts on pet parenting
- Travel tips for pets
- Celebrations – of life, weddings, birthdays, etc.
- And more!

This fun and uplifting resource is more than a magazine, it is an important part of the larger, inspiring and supportive PetPix World community open to all pet lovers and supports pet charity organizations.

For more information, please see **www.petpixworld.com.** You can buy a subscription to the magazine for $9.95 on the website for the digital version and a print copy can be purchased on Amazon.

DOGUE Magazine by @ Coverdogs
@thedoguemagazine
www/thedoguemagazine.com

According to their website, "DOGUE is the revolutionary and one-of-a-kind fashion magazine for the barkers that breaks the barriers between dog and human fashion. Its style and design are unprecedented and created specifically for, and by, the millennials. [Side note from me: I am most certainly not a millennial ~ and I absolutely adore DOGUE!]

"Launched digitally in 2019, as the first DOGUE magazine on Instagram, it is quickly becoming the authoritative bark in dog's fashion and beauty. Published monthly, our creative content now appears across print, digital and social media platforms, reaching a worldwide audience of fashion furward, dog-loving humans."

I asked Olianna, the Founder, Creative Director & Editor in Chief of DOGUE, a few questions. Here are her intriguing answers!

How did you get the idea to start ~ why did you start DOGUE? Your Story?

"I was working as a graphic designer when I came across a fun 'dogs in food' edits page on Instagram that really inspired me. So, I started creating dogs in food edits for my own pup. Then, others began asking me to create edits for them, so I created a dogs in food edits page on Instagram called **@puppyliciousedits**.

"And then, a year later, someone contacted me with a special request. She said, 'I want my pup inside a martini glass, but I also want you to make it look like a magazine cover, and put DOGUE on top of it.' I said, 'sure, why not!' So, I searched Instagram for DOGUE edits, to use as an example, but I couldn't find any, so I created my own DOGUE logo, and the rest is history!

"Soon after, a lot of requests followed, and I realized that I needed a separate edits page, for magazine covers, and I wasn't going to stop at DOGUE. So, I created **Barker's Bazbark**, inspired by Harper's Bazaar, for high fashion dogs, **Spawrts Illustrated**, inspired by Sports Illustrated, for sporty pups, and **National Pawgraphic**, inspired by National Geographic, for traveling pups.

"For two years, my page @coverdogs hosted digital magazine covers of these 4 magazines. And then people started asking me if DOGUE was a real magazine. First, I'd laugh of course, and say, 'No, it is just for fun. Think of it as artwork that you can post, print and frame.'

"And then, after getting more and more requests for a print magazine, I thought, 'Why not?' I did more research and I realized that while there were many dog magazines out there in the world already, there was not a dog fashion magazine that looked like Vogue.

"And so that's what I created. DOGUE Magazine looks different than all the other dog magazines."

How has it morphed into the empire it is today?

"The magazine became popular pretty quick, and has become my full-time job. I feel like this was my calling all along, because this work combines four of my biggest passions: dogs, writing, graphic design and fashion.

"The DOGUE Magazine and the Coverdogs community are both

growing rapidly. This year we are launching a Mobile App called "Coverdogs" to allow people to create their own dog magazine covers with just one click, and turn their pups into stars, instantly. The app is scheduled to be launched in October of this year (2022), on iOS and Android."

You can learn more about this exciting app here:
https://cover-dogs.com/app/

II – BOOKS
A few you might enjoy:

"Behind the Scenes: The Mysteries of the Dogs of Instagram"
by Louise Hall Reider

In this book you will get a sneak peek behind the scenes of the crazy, fun, intriguing and confusing world of the dogs on Instagram. It is the companion book to this social calendar and its inspiration!

"EAT, PLAY, LOVE (your dog)"
by Lara Shannon

The book every dog owner needs to provide their dog with the healthiest and happiest life possible.

"World of Dogs: A Book for Dog Lovers All over the World"
By Lara Shannon

This gorgeous little book celebrates the role of dogs in society, pop culture and our families around the world. It delves into the evolution and legacy of our canine companions.

"The Dog Went Over the Mountain: Travels with Albie"
 by Peter Zheutlin

This New York Times bestselling author of "Rescue Road" tells of his cross-country journey with his dog.

Here are a few Kindle Books we found on Amazon:

"How To Make Your Pet Instagram Famous | How I Grew My Pet's Instagram to 50,000 Real, Organic Followers & How You Can Too!"
By Samuel & Jen Huber

"How to Make Your Pet an Instagram Star: A step by step formula to help make your pet famous on Instagram"
By Drew Turner

III – BLOGS

Blog.hootsuite.com/dogs-of-instagram
Tells of 10 uber InstaFamous dogs with millions of followers

Greenfieldpuppies.com/blog/
Lots of information on this blog from the site that can help you find the perfect new dog by adoption

gopetfriendly.com/blog/
Specializes in travel tips for pet owners

dailydogstuff.com/blog/
Offers helpful info on behavior, health, food and other topics

bodieontheroad.com/blog/blog-masonry/bodie-blog/
Very fun dog-themed travel blog

More Inspiration

e.g. Dogster Magazine

Modern Dog Magazine

More Inspiration

More Inspiration

Chapter 21

More Inspiration ~ Websites I Love
& Other Social Media

More Inspiration

More Inspiration

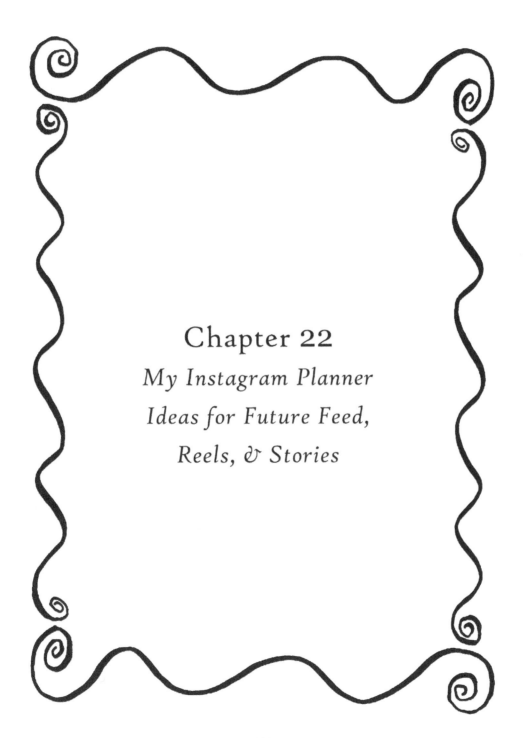

Chapter 22

*My Instagram Planner
Ideas for Future Feed,
Reels, & Stories*

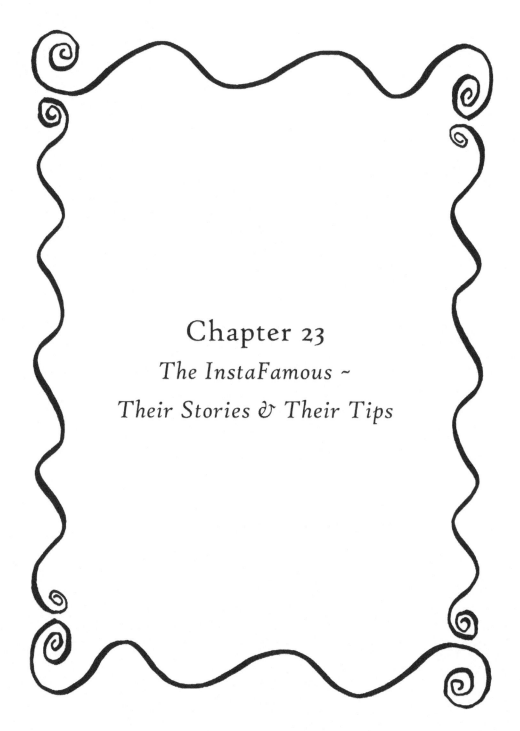

Chapter 23
The InstaFamous ~
Their Stories & Their Tips

Chapter 23
The InstaFamous ~ Their Stories & Their Tips

It is always so fascinating to hear the stories of InstaFamous dogs! In this section these influencers give us their "Cliff Notes" on their successful Instagram journeys.

Chiffon the Maltipoo
@chiffonthemaltipoo

With almost 150K followers, this is what Chiffon's Mom had to say:

Please tell me how you started and why.

"I originally started our Instagram page to have a collection of precious memories to look at. Chiffon brings me limitless love and so much happiness. As our following grew, I wanted to share her joy with everyone! I love hearing about the joy that Chiffon brings to people that follow her."

How did you grow your account to almost 150K followers?

This is how she did it and her advice:

"Keep Sharing Posts:
I shared a post every day without fail for over 4 years! Over these years,

at times my account didn't even grow at all and other times, it grew slowly but surely.

"Create Genuine Friendships:
I've met a lot of friends on Instagram that I keep up with and they always keep up with my posts too. I try to respond to comments as well and connect with followers!

"Viral Reels:
There has only been one time when I grew my account fast and that was just this year with a viral Instagram Reel. After that Reel, I started to post more of the type of Reels that my followers liked best. For me it was Chiffon's get ready with me videos where she picks her own accessories and gets dressed for an activity.

Please give us a few tips you have discovered along the way.

1. Tips are always changing as Instagram makes updates! But following along with the current changes and trends is a great way. If there is a new feature, I would do it!
2. If there is something that works for you, keep doing it. It can be the topic, the style or the trend.
3. You must find joy in sharing on Instagram! If you don't find it fun and or interesting, step back and see what it is you actually want to share.

Miss Dior
@iammissdior_

The story of this InstaFamous tiny fashionista started in a coffee shop in Australia. The barista saw how darling Dior was and announced that she must have an Instagram account. It became a fun little diary at first.

One day it was cold so Dior's Mummy posted her in a pretty sweater and it grew from there to 10K followers in the first year. She was often asked to promote products or model clothes.

By staying true to her brand and style she reached 20K followers and was then able to be very selective on her gigs. She started a business account and charged appropriately for her posts.

Some sincere and important advice comes from Dior's talented Mummy, who has a marketing background:

"Some seem to promote too many products rather than being selective and choosing to work with brands that suit them, their lifestyle and which they believe in. I am asked for Dior to promote dog chew products such as pig ears, kangaroo tendons and the likes. These are not products that Dior enjoys and therefore I decline. It would be false advertising.

"A quality brand of dog collars, leads and bandanas contacted me asking if I would promote their brand. I liked their brand, designs and quality, so I agreed. The items arrived and they were oversized for

Dior. I had to use holdback clips in the photos to keep the items in place to promote! Aligning with the right products is paramount.

"I love photoshop and have to admit I have dabbled with it on some of Dior's photos. I only edit for fun. I recently saw a post of an older dog where his teeth were whitened to promote a dog toothbrush.

"This is really what I mean when saying people need to be true to their own brand rather than agreeing to accept free stuff.

"With all the changes across Instagram, Reels are currently the way to increase followers over the original still photos. Posting a Reel with the right audio can take a dog playing to a cute or comedy reel. If this is created well it is when the Reel can go viral or at least exceptionally well."

Miss Dior is now a highly sought-after, well compensated influencer with close to 70K followers.

Leo, Olivia & Jolie Maltese
Models/Pet Influencers/Fashionistas
@leo.olivia.jolie

This trio posts for "Daily Doses of Fun" and say they are spoiled siblings making life more sparkly, stylish and fun. I really enjoyed their Momager's answers to my questions!

Why did you start your account?

"I started the babies' account just for fun, they were such cute puppies and my intention was just to post their adventures. Things started to change once I dressed them up, attending birthday parties and other events. Our followers seemed to love their matching outfits. This was about when I realized they were the new IG fashionistas!"

How did you attract so many followers?

"I have always been into fashion, and I love photography, so I decided to give it a try and explore their different personalities. I created a persona for each of them. A lot of people ask me how do I make them pose...honestly though, I let them be free to do their own thing. Maybe their spontaneity is what has caused so much attention. As long as they are having fun, I am good."

Could you share any practical tips or pointers that you learned along the way of becoming so famous?

"Our first account was deleted, their first two years erased. I had to start all over again, from scratch. So, my point is that things are not always easy. We are far from a huge account (currently at about 25K followers), but as a good dog mom, I am very passionate, persistent and obsessed with my babies.

"I try my best to build a good relationship with their followers. I think it is very important to be kind and respectful, as this is something that is never out of style. Since the beginning I introduced myself. I think people relate and connect more when the see the person behind the account."

"Tips: Be creative, find your passion, be persistent, try to engage and connect with your followers as much as you can, ignore haters and have fun. All fur babies are amazing and each has a unique talent!"

Faith the Friendly Morkie Dog Model
@friendly.faith.the.morkie

Three-year-old Faith's mom, Judy, tells her story of how they currently have almost 30K followers:

"I started her Instagram account when Faith was just 4 months old. I had just lost my first dog and was looking for a way to share Faith growing up, but also to include my angel girl, Twinkles.

"I wasn't sure what to expect when I began posting but I quickly found out that there was a huge caring pet community.

"I posted at least two times a day and after one week I had gained 200 followers. Before I knew it, I had reached 2000 followers and it kept growing. So, I feel the key to grow your Instagram account is to be consistent in posting, speak from the heart, make sure to engage with your followers and use your platform to give back to the community.

"Most of all have fun!"

Ginger Devine
@ginger_doggie

This diva, fashionista, dog influencer has been on Instagram about 3 years and already has close to 40K followers!

Her momager thinks she grew so fast because of their consistent engagement and good content. They dressed up Ginger, took her out with them, attended events, introduced her to people and passed out her cute Ginger Doggie stickers.

They try and to use the account for good causes. They work with Green K9 to raise money for rescues, by donating clothes and products.

Having fun is important to them too. And their account is lots of fun in addition to the good works they do.

Ginger's Mom says her best advice is about engagement. Follow the accounts you like regardless of size and do not to assume because you have a small account that people won't follow you. If you do grow your account, she adds, don't unfollow accounts just because they are small…. stick with those that engage with you.

And her really good further advice, "Find your niche. Ginger isn't a dog that does tricks, but she loves to dress up and do photo shoots. I do a lot of interactive posts which are fun and popular. Don't promote anything on your page you wouldn't use yourself! Try to stay away from hot topics, like politics, money and religion on your posts. Stay neutral.

Avoid drama. If you get negative comments or DMS, don't respond. Delete the comment and block the account."

She spends a lot of time managing her account. She goes through her followers about once a month and any accounts that haven't posted or engaged; she unfollows, unless she was told they were going on a break. Since one can only follow 7500 accounts, it is important to make sure they aren't bots or old, inactive accounts.

Another piece of her important advice is, "If you get any DMs from accounts that want you to click a link or go to another site, careful! Anything that looks off (even from an account you follow) be very careful. A lot of hackers operate that way. I do not click outside links. For example, if I get a DM from an account that wants me to promote them, I never click any links they say. Instead, I go to their page and investigate to see if they are legit. My general rule is if it seems too good to be true, it probably is!"

Chapter 24
Checklist ~
To Like, Comment & Save

Chapter 25
New Accounts to Consider

Chapter 25

New Instagram Accounts to Follow

Here is some space to list accounts to consider following:

Instagram Account	Notes:
eg. @Lady.Bouj	Author's tiny Chocolate Shihtzu
@Glamchisters	Stylish Chi Sisters support causes

Instagram Account　　　　Notes:

Instagram Account   **Notes:**

Instagram Account   **Notes:**

Instagram Account   **Notes:**

Chapter 26

35 Ways to Spread Kindness
on Instagram

Chapter 26
35 Ways to Spread Kindness on Instagram

Like so many on IG, we understand the most important advice is to be kind. We never really know what others might be going through behind the scenes.

Even the smallest gesture can make a big impact on the day. There are so many ways to spread kindness around the Gram! Here is a collection that furiends have suggested. You most likely already practice these little acts of kindness, as we try to ~ but it is inspiring to see them listed here.

Positivity and kindness have a ripple effect. What we do for others comes back to us tenfold. I like to read through these ideas from time to time, as little reminders, and to think of more ways to "sprinkle kindness around IG like confetti!"

1. Post uplifting messages
2. Think before you click
3. Remember the Golden Rule ~ to treat others as you wish to be treated
4. Be encouraging of friends' endeavors & activities
5. Send DMs of thanks and support
6. Spread love not hate
7. Share an inspiring post, quote or article
8. Promote a small business

9. Follow online friends, groups & communities that spread thoughtfulness
10. Be respectful
11. Use Instagram as a global village noticeboard for good causes
12. Make someone laugh – the best medicine!
13. Resist responding with anger – everyone has a bad day
14. Think the best of people
15. Practice positivity
16. Share good news
17. Show gratitude
18. Spread the word about worthwhile dog charity organizations
19. Promote someone else's work or account
20. Pay a compliment
21. Share your IG tips
22. Practice positive IG habits – Like, Comment & Save
23. Send DMs of support to friends you appreciate & admire
24. Donate to a good cause – even a small contribution
25. Write positive reviews for places, products & books you enjoy
26. Use kindness quotes in posts & ideas for random acts of kindness
27. Share your knowledge freely
28. Mentor someone on IG
29. Let people know you appreciate them
30. Get inspired – go to #randomactsof kindness
31. Say nothing if you have nothing good to say
32. Don't take the bait if something angers you – move on or keep scrolling
33. Practice kindness on yourself with quality self-care
34. Consider sponsoring & supporting a worthy cause
35. Explore & discover new friends/accounts that promote kindne

More Ways to Spread Kindness on IG

More Ways to Spread Kindness on IG

Chapter 27
My Personal Notes

Note from the Author

It has been a delight to put this whimsical social calendar and address book together for you! The idea and inspiration came about in answer to a common challenge I found with the many dog moms and dads interviewed for my first book – **one place to keep track of everything IG.**

That said, I am most certainly not an IG expert, nor pretend to be! It is my hope you have enjoyed the chapters and will find it useful to streamline your life behind the scenes of Instagram.

As you fill in the pages with your practical information and fanciful delights, let me know if there is a section you feel might be missing, that could be included for future editions. You can reach me at LouiseHallReider@gmail.com.

Don't forget to check out the bonus gift of the downloadable address book and holiday card tracker, if you are digitally inclined.

Thanks so very much for being here. When you have a moment, I would be so grateful if you could write a review on Amazon. It will help other like-minded dog igers to find our books.

Every best wish for your happiness on IG and beyond!
From my heart,
Louise

Book Bonuses

www.louisehallreider.com/bonuses

Type in the link above to receive your thank you bonuses:

- **Free Gift** to download a digital version of Holiday Card Tracking spreadsheet & Address Book

- **Coupon** for PetPix Academy World's Courses

- **Exclusive** Behind the Scenes video of Boujee's Boudoir

- A free email subscription for notifications of **upcoming book releases** by Louise & Boujee

About the Author

Louise Hall Reider has always been fascinated with people and their cultures around the world. She majored in broadcasting at university, after hosting TV and radio shows in her island home of Bermuda.

She has enjoyed a long and distinguished career in the incentive travel industry, having travelled to many diverse cultures spanning over 90 countries. She is well known among her global colleagues, family and friends as a great lover of dogs.

With the onset of social media, Louise became intrigued with the new culture of dogs on Instagram, and the lives of the people behind the carefully curated scenes. Her first book, **"Behind the Scenes: The Mysteries of the Dogs of Instagram ~ the Whys, Whats & Hows"** was published on Amazon in June, 2022.

Louise, her husband Dennis and their tiny Shih Tzu Boujee, divide their time between the Pacific Northwest, Maryland's Eastern Shore and Bermuda.

To learn more about Louise and Boujee you can connect with them at:
LouiseHallReider.com
LouiseHallReider@gmail.com
Pinterest.com/Louise Hall Reider
Instagram.com/Lady.Bouj

Made in the USA
Monee, IL
01 January 2023

24169372R00151